Stories for

Year Olds

Stories for

Year Olds

Jane Riordan
James Newman Gray

bookoli

Contents

Double Trouble

This is George and this is Woody.

Two cheeky brothers who don't always agree.

"I want to go up."

"I want to go down."

"I want to stay at home."

"I want to go out."

"I want to go **fast.**"

"I want to go **slow.**"

"I say **YES!**"

"I say **NO!**"

George and Woody start to cry.

Woody **stomps** off.

George is alone. The gift looks smaller now he's on his own.

"I'm sorry, George."

"I'm sorry, Woody."

They pull off the paper together and what do they see?

Woody starts to build, laying tracks on the ground,
then George gets a train and pushes it around.

"Chuff," says Woody,

and George says, "Choo!"

Playing is much more fun with two!

Puddle Splash

There's a parcel for Little Fox.
It's big and lumpy.
It doesn't rattle or jingle.

What could it be?

Little Fox pulls at the paper. He sees something bright yellow. He tears a little more, **then more, then more ...**

... to find the brightest, shiniest pair of yellow boots that Little Fox has ever seen!

Little Fox wishes it would rain.
"I want to go **splish, splash, splosh**
in my new boots," he says.

But outside the sky is blue.
"No sign of rain today, Little Fox," says Daddy Fox.

The next morning, Little Fox races down the stairs to look outside. The sun is shining. The sky is blue.

"No sign of rain today, Little Fox," says Daddy Fox.

On the third day, the sky is still blue. The sun is still shining. Little Fox feels sad.

He stamps his feet and stares at his little yellow boots waiting by the door. Waiting for the rain, just like Little Fox.

When Little Fox wakes up the next morning, he hears a sound outside.

Spit ... spat ... spot.

Could it be?

Spit ... spat ... spot.

YES! The sky is dark, thunder rumbles. It's raining!

On go the boots and out goes Little Fox.

Jump!
Jump!
Hop!
Splash!

Little Fox loves puddle jumping. Little Fox loves puddle splashing.

Squelch! Splash!
Squelch! Splash!

"I wish it was a rainy day every day!" says Little Fox.

"Waiting for the rain," smiles Daddy Fox, "makes it even more special."

And at the end of the day, Daddy Fox puts the yellow boots next to the door, all ready for the next rainy day.

I Don't Want to Go to Bed

"Bedtime for busy puppies," says Mama Dog.

"I am **NOT** going to bed!" says Little Pup.

Little Pup runs away and hides inside a bucket.

Mama Dog soon finds her.

"Come on, bedtime for busy puppies," says Mama Dog.

"I am **NOT** going to bed!" says Little Pup.

She runs, skips,
and jumps into the
house to hide
in the bathtub!

Mama Dog soon
finds her.

"Come on, bedtime
for busy puppies,"
says Mama Dog.

"I am **NOT** going to bed!" says Little Pup.

She bounces, boings, and bumps back outside. This time Little Pup hides inside the shed.

"Now I don't have to go to bed!" smiles Little Pup.

But it's cold in the shed.

It's dark in the shed.

Little Pup doesn't like hiding anymore.

Quick as a flash, Little Pup bounces, skips and jumps,

out of the shed,

over the bucket,

past the bathtub,

and straight into ...

... BED!

“Night, night busy puppies,” smiles Mama Dog.
But Little Pup is already fast asleep.

Why Do Cows Go 'Moo'?

This is Kitty. He's just turned two,
"**Why,**" he asks, "do cows go 'moo'?"

"Because," smiles his dad, "it's their special way,

of wishing you a wonderful day."

Kitty stares at the rain with a frown.

"**Why,**" he asks, "does water fall down?"

"If up was down and down was up,
you'd have no milk left in your cup!"

Kitty stands with his back against the wall.

"**Why,**" he asks, "am I so small?"

"You're my little acorn," says Dad, in reply.

"With sun and rain, you'll soon reach the sky."

As the stars come out, it's time for bed.

"Why," Kitty asks, "can't I play instead?"

"Your toys," says Dad, "are fast asleep.
Sweet dreams little question boy, don't make a peep."

"**Why,**" Kitty asks, as his eyes start to close.
Then he drifts off into a deep, happy doze.

I Can Do It!

Rosie and Maisie and little Flo,
All of them hopping, all on the go.

Rosie's in front

and Maisie's behind,

Flo's at the back
but she doesn't
seem to mind.

"I can do it," you'll hear Flo say.

"I may be small but I'll do it my way."

They come to a tree that's blocking the track.
Rosie climbs, Maisie jumps, then they both look back...

It's too high for Flo but she has a plan
To squeeze through a gap as quick as she can.

"I can do it," you'll hear Flo say,
"I may be small but I'll do it my way."

They come to a stream and
Rosie makes the leap.

Next is Maisie, who lands in a heap.

But Flo finds a log and makes a little boat.

It wobbles, it jiggles

but it stays afloat.

"I can do it," you'll hear Flo say,
"I may be small but I'll do it my way."

They come to a garden
full of things to eat.

Rosie pulls,

Maisie tugs at a tasty treat.

But the carrot won't budge
until Flo comes along.

Out it pops! Flo is small but she's strong.

As the three bunnies sit in the shade of a tree,
Rosie munches, Maisie crunches, they do agree ...

"Flo can do it," they both say,
"She may be small but she does it her way!"

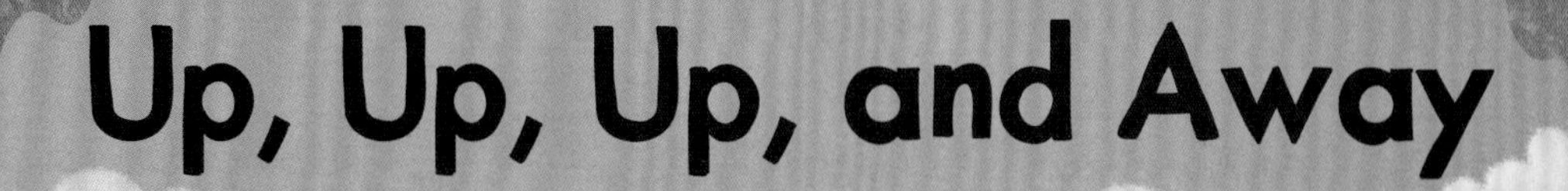

Up, Up, Up, and Away

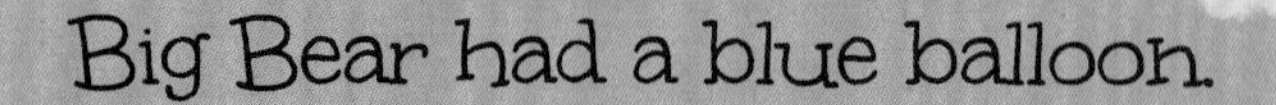

Big Bear had a blue balloon.

Little Bear had a green balloon.

And Baby Bear had
a red balloon.

Big Bear ran and jumped with his balloon.

Bounce!
Bounce!
Bounce!

Little Bear bopped his balloon.

Bop!
Bop!
Bop!

Baby Bear gazed at her balloon.

She didn't notice the string

slip, slip,

slipping through her paws.

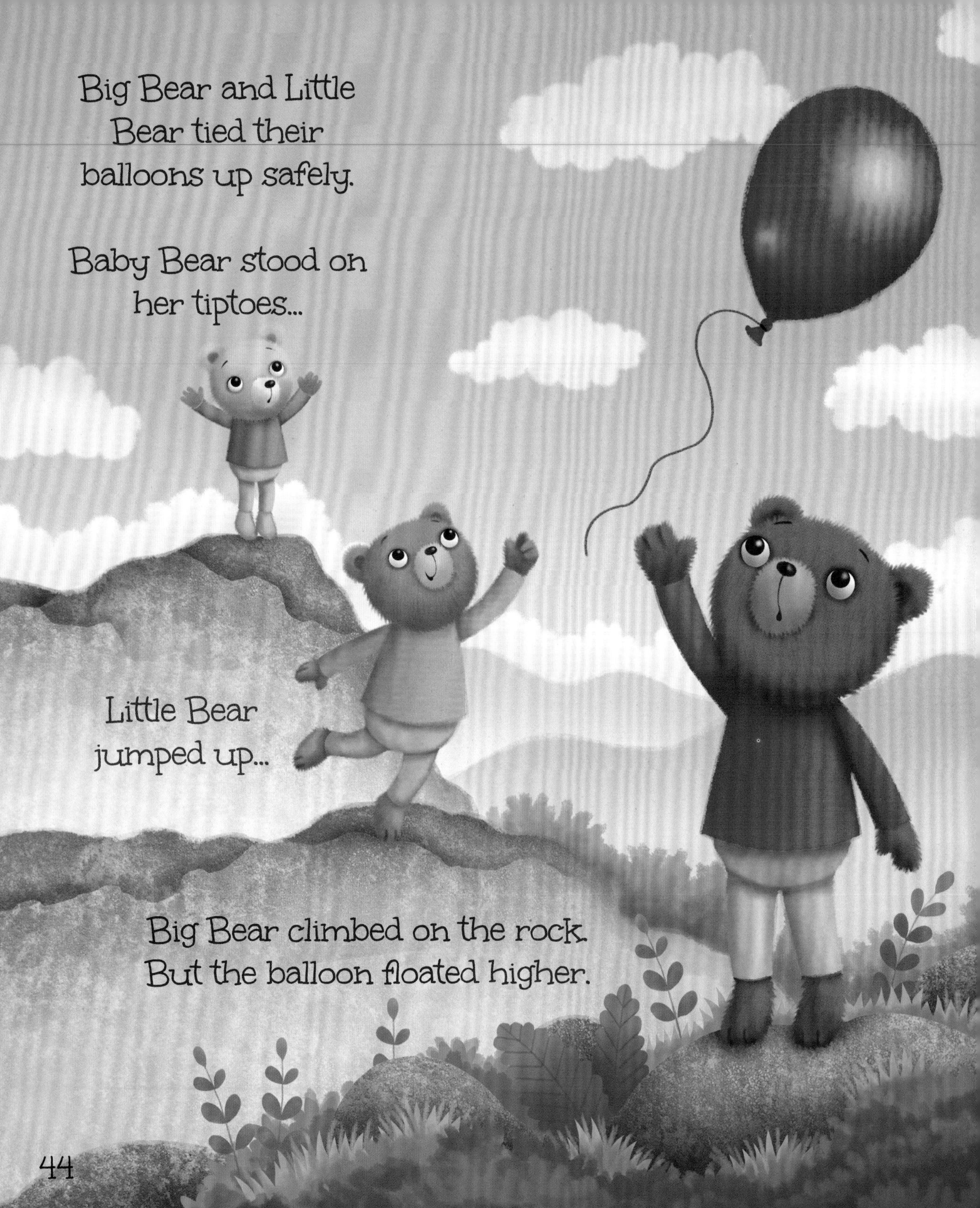

Big Bear and Little Bear tied their balloons up safely.

Baby Bear stood on her tiptoes...

Little Bear jumped up...

Big Bear climbed on the rock. But the balloon floated higher.

Soon Baby Bear's balloon was higher than the trees.

Baby Bear watched her balloon. She hoped that Big Bear and Little Bear didn't see the tear splash down her cheek.

Baby Bear imagined the balloon floating over fields,
floating over the town,
floating out to the ocean blue.

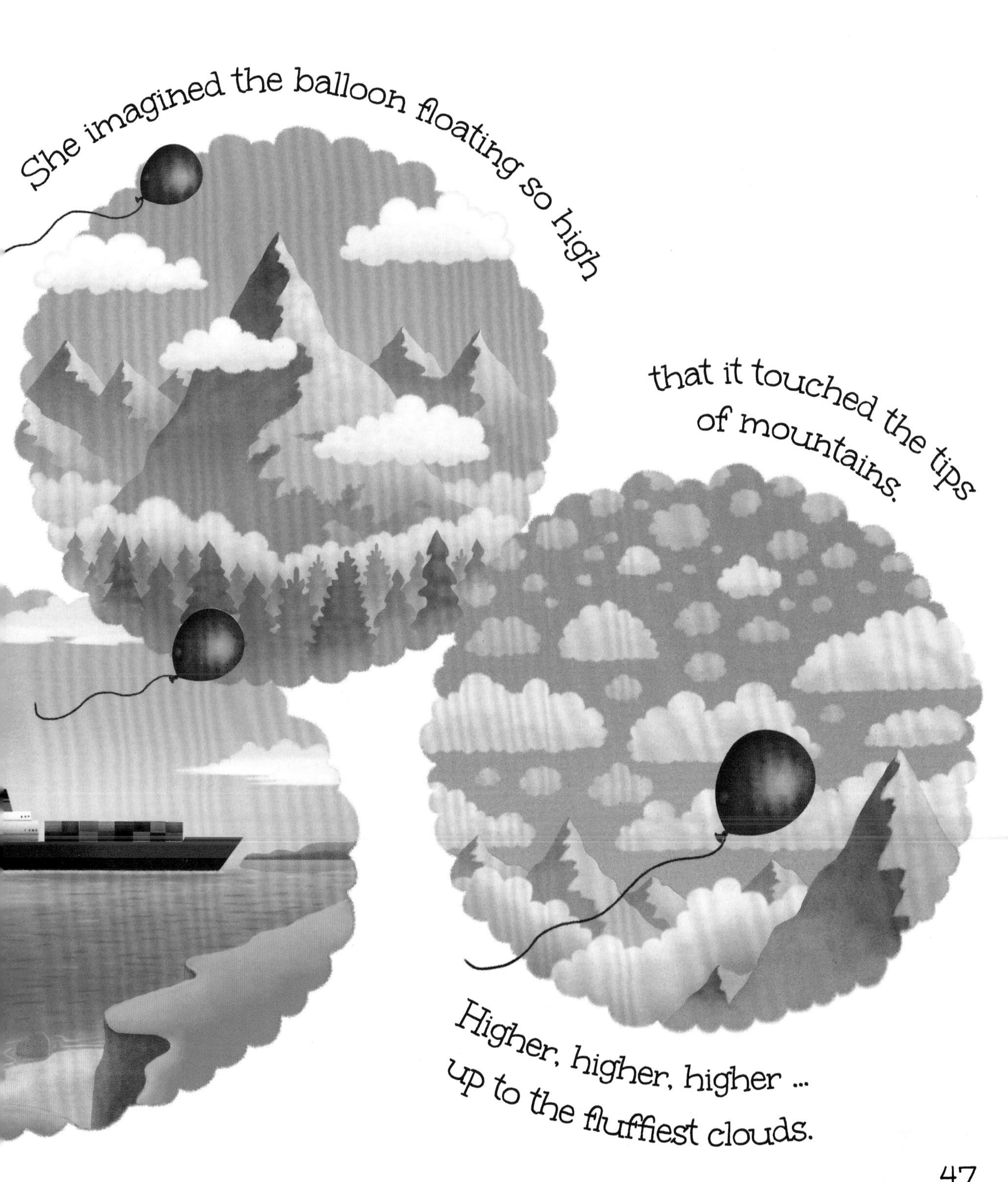

She imagined the balloon floating so high

that it touched the tips of mountains.

Higher, higher, higher ...
up to the fluffiest clouds.

By bedtime, Big Bear and Little Bear's balloons had been bopped until they popped.

But that night, in her dreams, Baby Bear's balloon flew on, past the stars, past the big, bright moon. And in her sleep, Baby Bear smiled.